Stories
about Linda and Lee

By Eleanor Thomas

With

Ernest W. Tiegs and Fay Adams

Ginn and Company

Boston · New York · Chicago · Atlanta · Dallas · Columbus · San Francisco · Toronto · London

Contents

Illustrations by JANET SMALLEY
and JEANNE McLAVY

Unit One · The Family

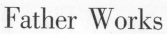

Father Works

Mother Works, Too

The Family Looks for a New House

They Find This House

The Family Moves

The family moves out of this house.
But they can not find Dusty.

The Family Moves

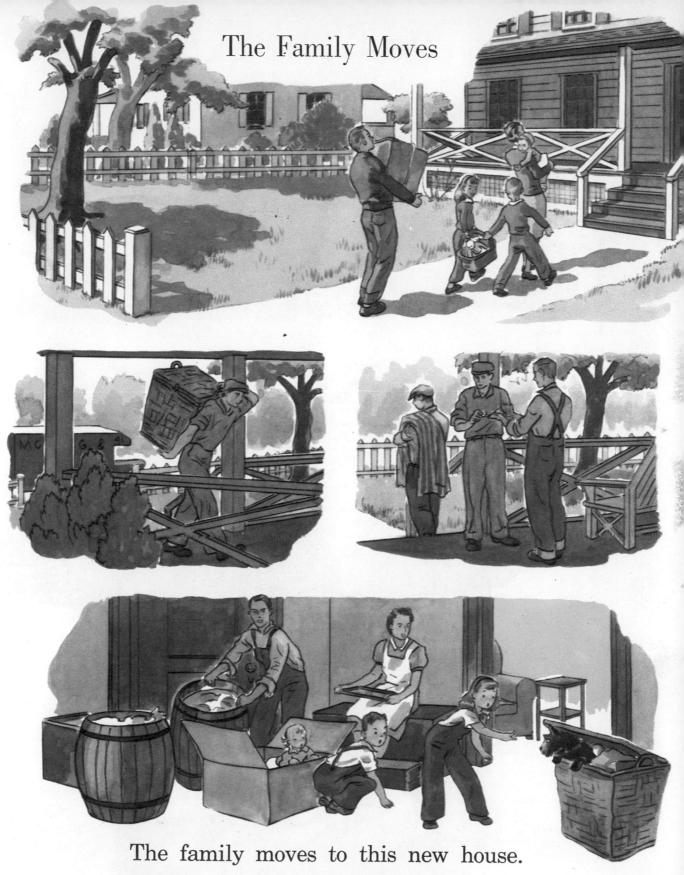

The family moves to this new house.
Where do they find Dusty?

Mother Makes the House a Home

Linda Helps Mother

Father Helps, Too

What does Father do?

How Does Lee Help?

Guess what Lee said to Mother.

The Family Cleans the Yard

Unit Two · Playtime

Linda and Lee Play with New Friends

The new friends are good friends.

Linda and Lee Know What to Do

See what they do.

On the Way to the Store

Who knows what to do?

In the Store

Who knows what to do?

Lee Has Fun

Linda Has Fun, Too

Fun at a Picnic

Linda helps Mother
at the picnic.

Linda keeps clean
at the picnic.

Look! Look at Lee!
Did he keep clean at the picnic?

The Circus

The children get ready for a circus.

The Circus Parade

The children get ready for the parade.

This is the circus parade.
Who is in the parade?

Fun at the Circus

See what the children take to the circus.

Fun at the Circus

The children work to make the circus fun.

Unit Three · What Linda and Lee Learn at Home

Time to Go to Bed

What does Linda do at bed time?

Time to Go to Bed

What does Lee do at bed time?

Time to Get Up

Mother does not help Lee.

Mother does not help Linda.

Find the Safe Way

Find the Safe Way

Lee Learns the Safe Way

How did the toy get here?

Lee picks up the toy.

He puts it away.

Who Went the Safe Way?

Where are Linda and Lee?

Look at this plant.
Lee picks this plant.

Lee does not know
where to go.

Father Finds Lee

Lee will not pick this plant again.

On a School Day

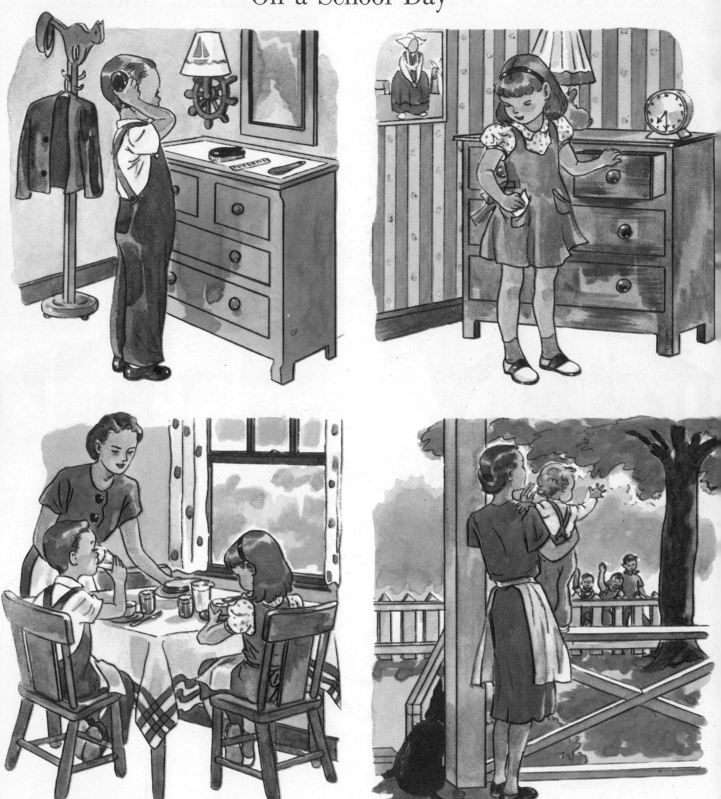

How do Linda and Lee get ready for school?

On the Way to School

At School

Linda and Lee are happy at school.

Where Are the Children?

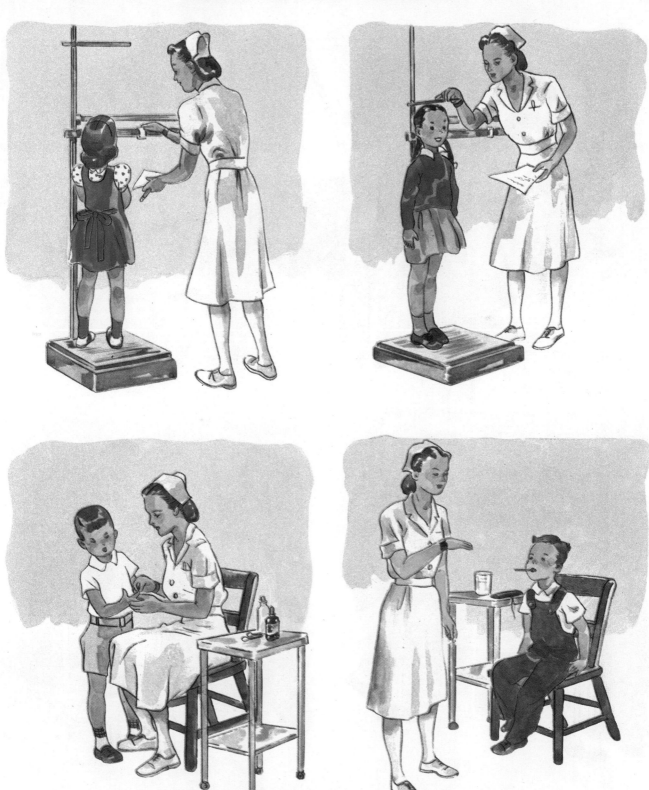

This friend helps the children.

The Children at Work

This is what the children make.
Can you guess what it is?

Books at School

Who knows how to use books?

Linda Helps at School

Linda Helps at School

The Children Eat at School

What will Linda eat?

What will Lee eat?

A Clean-up Day at School

The school yard is not clean.
Who will help clean up the yard?

A Clean-up Day at School

This is clean-up day.

The children clean the school yard.

At Work Out of Doors

Linda does not want Nan to stop.

Find the children who do not listen.

Linda Likes to Paint

Linda does not listen to Fred.

Linda listens to Tom.

Why did she listen?

The Children Clean Up

The Children Get Ready for a Party

Patsy wanted to help Linda.
But see what she did.

Patsy looked at the water.
Lee did something to help.

The Party at School

Play at School

Mary stops the fun.

This will not be fun for Lee.
He will not want to play with Fred again.

Play at School

Find the safe way to play.

Linda and Lee have fun.
But Patsy does not have fun.

Is This a Safe Way to Play?

A Band at School

Tom learns how to be happy at work.

The Band Learns to Play

This is a good band.

Why is it a good band?

Unit Six · Pets for Linda and Lee

Lee gets a fish.

He wants the fish for a pet.

Lee can not keep the fish.

Do you know why?

New Pets for School

This is a pet store.

The children get some fish for pets.

The fish get something to eat.

The children keep the fish clean.

A Little Yellow Bird

The bird likes to keep clean.

See what the bird eats.

The children are good to the bird.

A Little Black Hen

A little black hen comes to school.

This will not do.

Where can the children keep the little black hen?

A Chicken House at School

The children make a little house.
It is a chicken house.

The chicken house is in the school yard.
The chicken house has a yard, too.

A New Pet for Linda and Lee

Where are Father and Linda and Lee?
They are here to get a kitten.

This is the way to pick up a kitten.

The Kitten at Home

The kitten looks at the new home.
The kitten has something to eat.

Linda said, "This is Cinders."
Cinders has a good home.

Dusty and Cinders

Lee said, "You are a good dog, Dusty."
Linda said, "You are good to our kitten."

Dusty likes the new kitten.
Cinders plays with Dusty.

Cinders at Play

Why did Linda put Cinders in the yard?

Cinders can not get down.
What does Father do?

Dusty Learns to Be Good

Dusty gets on a chair.

Lee said, "Stop, Dusty!"
Dusty will not do this again.

What Did Dusty Learn Here?

Dusty is a good dog.

Father pets Dusty.

Mr. Green Comes to Town

Mr. Green said, "Will you come to see my farm?"
Guess what the children said.

The Children Will Go to the Farm

Linda and Lee can go to the farm.

How do you know?

In Town

The children see stores.

They see a train.

They see this in town.
What is it?

Now they ride
out of town.

On the Way to the Farm

The children see the airport.

They see a boat.

They see a farm truck.

They see Mr. Green and Jane.

This Is the Barn

The big dog helps
the farmer.

Jane said, "We keep
horses here."

Jane said, "We like to have
kittens in the barn."

Tom went up the ladder.
What did he see?

Cows on the Farm

The cows will go to the barn.
The farmer will milk the cows.

The farmer gets
the cows ready to milk.

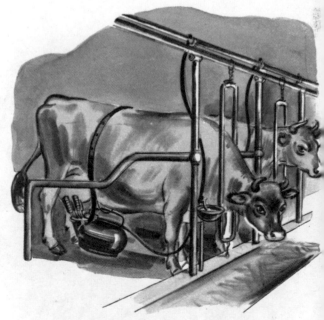

Some farmers milk
this way.

Some farmers milk
this way.

What Are These Animals?

These horses work on the farm.　These animals like to eat.

These animals like to play.　The ducks like water.

Baby Chickens on the Farm

Mr. Green puts eggs in here.

Baby chickens will come out of the eggs.

The baby chickens are in this house.

The baby chickens will not be cold in here.

Work on the Farm

What does the farmer use for this work?

What does the farmer use on the apple trees?

The farmer will plant wheat.

What did the farmer see?

Work on the Farm

What does Mrs. Green do here?

Mrs. Green gets
the eggs.

Mrs. Green puts the eggs
in boxes.

A Party at the Farm

The Children Go Home

"We like your farm,"
said Linda.

"Thank you for a good
time," said Patsy.

"Come again," said Jane.
"Thank you," said the children.

A Farm at School

The children make this farm.

THE
NORTH LANE FAIR

Does Lee Keep What He Finds?

Lee finds something at the fair.

Lee will not keep it.

See where he takes it.

What Jane Sees at the Fair

Mr. Green's animals come to the fair.

Mrs. Green's apple pie comes to the fair.

Fun at the Fair

Shoes for the Horses

The horses get new shoes.
The children get little horse shoes.

The Little Black Hen at the Fair

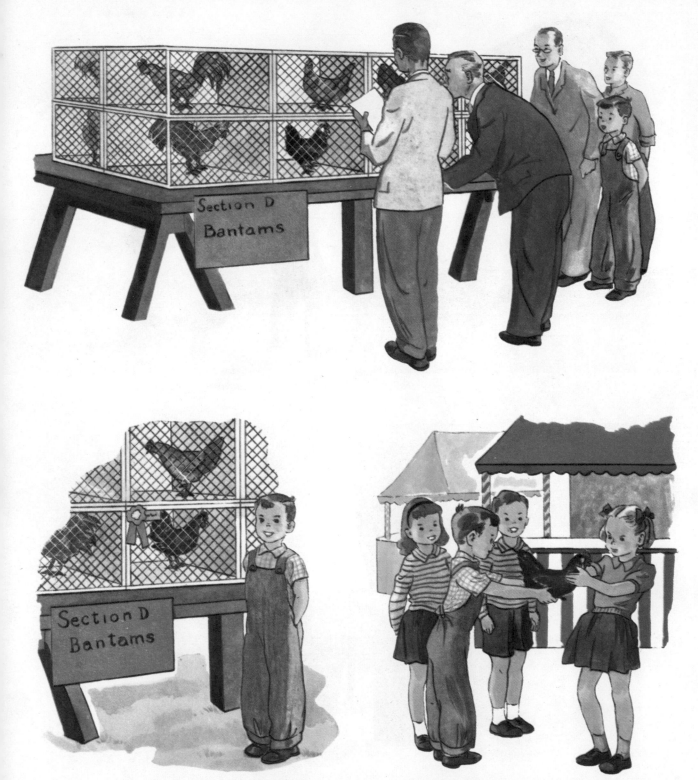

Tom said, "This is for you. Please keep
my little black hen on your farm."

A Surprise for the Children

Notes to the Teacher

Content and Organization

Important objectives of the social studies include giving the child the experiences, knowledge, and understandings which function as the basis of democratic attitudes, problem-solving ability, and desirable behavior.

With these objectives in mind, *Stories about Linda and Lee* has been written around the lives of typical five- and six-year-olds. It depicts their family life, incidents which take place in their school, and their neighborhood experiences. It takes them beyond the immediate environment to a near-by farm, and it introduces them to such a typical community enterprise as a small county fair.

This volume has been developed through eight major units of activity:

1. The Family
2. Playtime
3. What Linda and Lee Learn at Home
4. School Days for Linda and Lee
5. Fun at School
6. Pets for Linda and Lee
7. Mr. Green's Farm
8. The Fair

Social-studies objectives appropriate to children of these ages have been developed in connection with these interest centers.

Using the Picture Stories

The ability of the first-grade child to understand social-studies concepts presented in picture and verbal form greatly exceeds his ability to read printed words. Consequently, the content of this volume is presented largely through picture stories, each of which consists of illustrations portraying an incident, a process, or an activity which contributes to the child's attainment of one or more social-studies objectives.

Since little or no reading ability can be assumed on the part of most first graders at the beginning of the school year, the teacher should read to the children the titles and other textual matter related to a given series of pictures. As the pupils gain in reading proficiency, they may be allowed to read the text for themselves. However, the teacher should not suggest independent reading until the children are fully ready for it, and she should at all times protect the self-esteem of those who cannot read.

The pictures should be examined from left to right, thus helping the children form a habit which will be useful as they learn to read print. The teacher must be sure that every child understands the meaning of each picture as well as the story which each sequence tells. She should ask questions which bring out essential information and should encourage contributions and suggestions from the class which will lead the pupils to attain the major understandings and the objectives of each sequence.

The Vocabulary

Only 160 different words were used in writing *Stories about Linda and Lee*. Of these 116 are from the vocabulary of the Pre-primers and Primer of the Ginn Basic Readers and are assumed as known words. The remaining 44 words are considered new. No more than two new words appear on any page of *Stories about Linda and Lee* and each one is used at least four times.

Complete information about the vocabulary, together with lists of the known words and the new words, are given in the *Teacher's Manual*.

The Teacher's Manual

A manual is provided to help teachers understand the objectives of each unit and lesson and to suggest methods for attaining these objectives.

These lesson plans contain such aids as the following:

1. Ways to introduce each unit or area of interest.

2. General understandings, attitudes, skills, and behavior patterns to be stressed for each lesson.

3. Ways to introduce and develop concepts through picture interpretation.

4. Activities which may be used to enrich and extend social understandings.

5. Suggested techniques for checking and evaluating the child's progress.

Special emphasis has been placed upon teacher-pupil planning, doing, and evaluating. Teachers are given definite, concrete suggestions for guiding children to democratic attitudes and practices.